DO BETTER

LEADERSHIP MANUAL

We cannot do better if we don't know
better. However, it's our responsibility
to get the information to do better.

ROBENS CHERY

It is insanity to know *better* and not do *better*, but expect *better*.

Robens Chery

Library of Congress Cataloging-in-Publication Data

ISBN # 978-1-7379938-5-8

©2022 Robens Chery

Publisher: Principle House Publishing
P.O. Box 190453
Lauderhill, Florida 33319

Cover Design by Evoke180 Publishing

Interior design and formatting by Evoke180 Publishing

CONTENTS

Name:

_____

Date

_____

Organization

_____

INTRODUCTION

My name is Robens Chery, and I'm the founder and Senior Pastor at Revelation Christian Church in Broward County, Florida. RCC is a multicultural non-denominational ministry striving to reveal Christ on the earth.

Every year, between the months of September and October, God would begin to speak to me regarding the upcoming year and how I, as a shepherd, should lead the church spiritually. The word that came to me during my quiet time was "Awaken." God wanted me to teach the congregation to wake up, because life is not over and we still have work to do in every area in our lives.

During the month of January 2022, we started a series entitled "AWAKEN FOR PURPOSE." The congregation was excited about the sermons because during the pandemic, most of us needed a wake-up call. We allowed the pandemic to shift our minds from active individuals to passive individuals. We became hopeless, depressed, tired, disappointed and lazy.

(2 Timothy 1:6) *For this reason I remind you to fan into flame the gift of God, which is in you through the laying on of my hands.*

Truth be told, we are simply hurting, in disbelief, and too emotionally unstable to pursue any goals that God had placed in our hearts pre-pandemic. The pandemic disrupted our rhythm; many of us are still trying to recover. During our second service in the series "Awaken," the phrase "DO BETTER" came up in the message and every time I said it, I felt something behind it. I felt God was trying to tell me something. I remember that Sunday, I said to the congregation that God was calling us to "DO BETTER" in every area in our lives, especially in ministry. After praying, I realized the title for the following month's series would be "DO BETTER." As I began to prepare for the "DO BETTER" series, I received revelations on how to do better myself and help my flock do the same.

We all have areas in our lives we know need to be improved—they need to be better. In this manual, we will talk about how to do better and the importance of doing better. Many of us want to see better in our personal, financial, and mental lives among other things. However, we are expecting better to come from the outside rather than from within. Or we want to do better, but are not willing to put in the work.

(REVELATION)- You cannot demand better if you have not taken the necessary steps for better.

Reflection (In your own words)

_____

_____

_____

_____

_____

_____

We live in a world where everything around us is constantly evolving. If we are not striving to do better or be better in every area in our lives, from ministry to relationships, business, personal, financial, and health matters, we risk becoming irrelevant and outdated. A *has-*

been business or ministry will lose its flavor and eventually die. Many of us want to do better in our finances, health, and relationships, but we don't know where to start. For many of us, getting started is the number-one challenge.

We can get so comfortable doing something or being the same way for a long time, even when we realize the way we have been working and thinking needs to change. We often find it very difficult to reset and start anew.

(REVELATION) -*Doing better starts with us.*
We must stop expecting others to do better when we ourselves are not striving for better.

Reflection *(In your own words)*

_____

_____

_____

_____

_____

_____

(REVELATION)-*The expectation of better only comes and is received from a person who's doing better.*

Reflection *(In your own words)*

_____

_____

_____

_____

_____

In this manual, I will share with you the revelation God revealed to me regarding the road to better. Are you ready? Well, investing in this manual was the first step in getting better. Congratulations, you are now on the road to becoming a better you, which will make everything around you better as well. I pray that you will take this journey seriously and follow the guidelines and principles to a better you. LET'S GO!!!

Define better:

_____

_____

_____

_____

_____

_____

Define mediocrity:

_____

_____

_____

_____

_____

_____

Define success:

_____

_____

_____

_____

_____

_____

What are your goals for this year?

_____

_____

_____

_____

_____

How do you plan to achieve them?

_____

_____

_____

_____

_____

List five obstacles you foresee that can be a roadblock to achieving your goals.

_____

_____

_____

_____

_____

List five distractions in your life now.

_____

_____

_____

Where do you see yourself five years from now?

_____

_____

_____

_____

_____

_____

_____

_____

_____

_____

_____

_____

_____

What motivates you?

_____

_____

_____

_____

_____

_____

_____

_____

_____

_____

_____

_____

_____

_____

SEASON 1

THE JOURNEY TO BETTER

It is difficult to do better if better doesn't start with us. We must be willing to take the necessary steps to improve ourselves in every area in our lives. Wanting better from others and not wanting better for ourselves is foolish. Many of us can clearly see the areas others need to develop, however, we find it difficult to see what we ourselves need to elevate.

(Matthew 7:4-5) *How can you say to your brother, 'Let me take the speck out of your eye,' when all the time there is a plank in your own eye? 5 You hypocrite, first take the plank out of your own eye, and then you will see clearly to remove the speck from your brother's eye.*

(REVELATION)-*You cannot help anybody until you can help yourself.*

Reflection (In your own words)

_____

_____

_____

_____

_____

_____

_____

_____

This chapter might be the hardest chapter in this manual. Remember every new season in your life begins with adjustments. I am going to ask you, please don't allow offense to stop you from becoming better. Many times we get very offended when we are being challenged by a leader or mentor to grow in certain areas in our lives.

(Revelation) *Better is for me.*

Reflection *(In your own words)*

_____

_____

_____

_____

_____

Proverbs 3:12 *Because the Lord disciplines those he loves, as a father the son he delights in.*

Better has to start with us! How many of us feel that there are areas in our lives where we can do better? Guess what? Every one of us can do better. Whatever the areas are, if we put our minds to becoming better, we can see results. However, if we believe we have arrived and there's no need to do better, we are fooling ourselves.

(Proverbs 28:26) *MSG "If you think you know it all, you're a fool for sure; real survivors learn wisdom from others."*

(Revelation) *No one knows it all. We all can do better.*

Reflection (In your own words)

_____

_____

_____

_____

_____

This manual doesn't have chapters but seasons, and that's done on purpose. In every season, there's a different you. Because we know that seasons change, we must also change or adapt to the season. I am not the same person I was two years ago. I had to do some growing up and take responsibility for where I was and where I am going. I don't think the same anymore, I don't act the same anymore, I don't get upset for the same reasons anymore. When I was younger, I used to allow people's opinions to affect me emotionally. And when I am emotional, I don't reason properly. I have changed. As I get older, I see myself maturing for the better. When you know better, you do better. Only a fool would know better and not do better and expect better. Once you know better, you behave better, produce better, and lead better. As the Senior Pastor of RCC, I am expected to lead the church in a manner worthy of the calling. I can no longer be led by my emotions; I have to manage my emotions in order to be an effective leader.

(1 Corinthians 13:11) *When I was a child I talked like a child, I thought like a child, I reasoned like a child. When I become a man, I put the ways of childhood behind me.*

We cannot do better if we don't know better. However, it's our responsibility to get the information to do better. Some would say, "I cannot be held responsible for better if I don't know better." If you don't know better, you should inquire about what is needed for better. The excuse of not knowing will only go so far. After a while the question will start to come up. What have you done to better yourself? What trainings or lessons have you taken to improve yourself, your relationships, your positions, your finances, and your health?

(1Timothy 4:15) *Be diligent in these matters; give yourself wholly to them, so that everyone may see your progress.*

(Revelation) *Better requires training.*

Reflection (In your own words)

We have to stop expecting others to do better when we ourselves are not willing to do better. If better doesn't start with us, it will be problematic to see better around us.

When I was a middle school reading teacher for Broward County Public Schools district, every year we had to take courses and training to either keep our certification or to adapt to new technology or curricula. The school board and the principal at each school were adamant about these training sessions. Even though these sessions were annoying at times, the fact of the matter was the school leaders wanted us to better ourselves in the areas we served. If we are better as teachers, the students will do and be better as well.

(Revelation) *A better you provides a better outcome.*

Reflection (In your own words)

_____

_____

_____

_____

_____

_____

One thing I have observed: every organization, whether profit or non-profit, has an expectation for better except the church. In my experience, people get offended when you ask them to better or improve themselves. When we feel insulted, it becomes difficult to receive the information needed for better. Asking for better may look or come out as a correction. However, correction is not an attack. Correction is asking people to improve themselves for the betterment of the organization and so that individuals can keep their positions. This is a fact that will take me to my next segment.

Better Requires Training

In every organization, there must be training for better. To have better leaders and employees, there must be a plan in place for growth. Training gives your organization a better chance to be more productive in every area. Growth requires training, training requires dedication, and dedication requires willing individuals who are excited about adding value to themselves and the company they serve.

Training should not be treated as a chore. The training should be fun, exciting, uplifting, and well planned. If we are excited about our position and enjoy what we do, then we should look forward to bettering ourselves through leadership training.

As a pastor, every year I attend leadership development not only to enhance my life, but also to add value to what I was called to do. Even though I was given a gift to serve as a pastor, it is my responsibility to develop my gift in order to better serve the people as I am called to do. I would be doing a disservice to God and to the people I am privileged to serve if I don't find ways to better myself.

Having a title doesn't negate me from getting better or asking for help. As a matter of fact, it's the opposite. The higher the title you carry, the more wisdom you need.

(Revelation) *The greatest leaders are the ones who have leaders around them.*

Reflection (In your own words)

_____

_____

_____

_____

_____

_____

Don't act like you know better and don't do better. You cannot do better by yourself. If you call yourself a doctor and wear doctor's clothing, you are expected to perform as a doctor. Whatever your title may be, you are expected to carry out the functions of that particular role. It is not wise to claim to know something when you have no understanding of its function. If you do this, you are a fraud.

Stop portraying yourself as someone who is skilled at something when you're not.

If you desire a position, learn the functions first before applying for the role. Doing better is not just for you, but for everyone connected to you. If I am supposed to be part of Christ's body and the part that I play in the body is not trained for better, then the parts I'm connected to in the body will malfunction and cause the rest of the body to break down. In order for the body to operate properly, every part must eventually master its role and purpose.

(1 Conrinthians 12:20-22) *But now there are many members, but one body. 21 And the eye cannot say to the hand, "I don't need you!" and the head cannot say to the feet, "I don't need you." 22 On the contrary, those parts that seem to be weaker are indispensable.*

(Revelation) *The part you play matters.*

Reflection (In your own words)

_____

_____

_____

_____

_____

_____

There are people in your organization who are holding a position and don't want to be better or get better. Even after the opportunity for better has been presented to them, they either feel entitled or that it's beneath them to get trained. Guess what? These people are dragging your organization down. There are others, on the other hand, who have undertaken the training to better themselves and have prepared themselves for better, yet because the position is not available, they continue to sit on the sidelines watching people holding vital positions with no intention to add value to themselves or the organization. And most of the time, they are friends and family members of the owners.

(Revelation) *Part of leadership is to make decisions that will help the organization grow.*

Reflection *(In your own words)*

_____

_____

_____

_____

_____

_____

It's unusual to see better or growth in any organization without training. The reason people take training in their fields is because they want to get better and be better. They want to advance the organization and themselves. The reasons others don't take training in their fields are because they don't have a desire for growth or they don't see themselves in that particular role for a long period of time.

Another hard pill to swallow is that some leaders and owners don't value advancement themselves; therefore they don't make it mandatory for employees to attend trainings. As a teacher, it was required to attend professional development courses. In conclusion, training is a vital component in every organization. When it's done properly, you will always grow.

(Revelation) *People will invest in their future.*

Reflection (In your own words)

Better Requires Vision

It's questionable to do better if you have not seen better. It is easier to become something or do something once you have seen it. As human beings, we are able to do a lot more when our vision is intact. Vision is an intricate part of human life. Without eyes, it would be very difficult for a person to navigate throughout the day because they cannot see where they are going. In the same manner, in the journey to do better, we must be able to see where we are going or have someone show us the way in order to achieve the growth we are looking for.

(Revelation) *Vision is an instrument to focus or refocus the original purpose.*

Reflection (In your own words)

(Proverbs 29:18) *Where there's no vision, the people perish; But he that keepeth the law, happy is he.*

I remember sitting under my pastors, Apostle Ed and Yvette, for eight plus years at Redeeming Word Christian Christian Center International (RWCCI). I learned so much during that season of my life and to tell you the truth, most of what I learned was through watching my pastors. The way they preached, the way they interacted with each other and people in general. The way they lived—I saw it all.

One day I had the chance to preach at RWCCI, I sounded just like Pastor Ed. Even though I had my own way of preaching, you could tell I sat under him. He gave me the confidence I needed to do what God called me to do on this level.

Vision is very important. What do you see? Do you see yourself growing? Write down what you see, in order to be able to execute your vision with precision.

(Habakkuk 2:2) *And the Lord answered me: Write the vision; make it plain on tablets, so he may run who reads it.*

Better Requires Preparation

I live in Florida, where the weather changes like the wind. However, there are hurricane seasons that every Floridian has to be ready for and if they are not prepared, it can cost them their lives. The best time to prepare is not during hurricane season, it's during the offseason. Things are cheaper, you are not in a hurry, and you can find everything you need to survive the season.

(Proverbs 6:6-8) *Go to the ant, O sluggard; consider her ways, and be wise. 7 Without having any chief, officer, or ruler, 8 She prepares the bread in summer and gathers her food in harvest.*

(Revelation) *Waiting for the perfect moment is costing you.*

Reflection *(In your own words)*

_____

_____

_____

_____

_____

_____

In the same way, better requires preparation. Don't wait until everything is falling apart to better yourself. Preparation is getting you ready for the future. Because you want to be better, it is wise to set aside what you need for better. Preparation requires time and sacrifice. You have to set time aside to prepare yourself for better. In every aspect of your life, you are going to need time to get better.

Better Requires Sacrifice

(Revelation) *Better is not a one-time quick fix, better is dedication and sacrifice.*

Reflection *(In your own words)*

_____

_____

_____

_____

What are you willing to give up to better yourself? Are you willing to give up your time, money, friends, and the things you love to do? With everything in life, if we want to grow in a particular area, we are going to have to make it a priority in order to see growth; not just any growth, real growth; improvement that can be sustained over time. It's time to stop saying we are ready to do better when we are not willing to be trained, prepared, or make sacrifices.

(1Timothy 4:15) *Be diligent in these matters; give yourself wholly to them, so that everyone may see your progress.*

We cannot continue to do things the way we used to and expect a different outcome. When we do this, we are expecting growth without sacrifice. God wanted to save humanity; He sacrificed His son Jesus to do so. If God had to make a sacrifice, we have to make one as well. For many of us, I don't think we are willing to make a sacrifice until it requires something we love or want. Sacrifices are never easy; however, they are for the better.

You are in a new season, and this season requires an upgrade. This season asks for a different version of you. A part of you no one has seen before. The old you cannot function in this new season. You've got to do better. So often we want to do better, but we are not willing to do the work for better.

(James 4:17) *If anyone, then, knows the good they ought to do and doesn't do it, it is a sin for them.*

No more excuses! There will be seasons when we won't know how to do better or how to be better, but once when we know better, we should do better.

(Revelation) *The expectation of better is only placed upon us when we know better.*

Reflection *(In your own words)*

_____

_____

_____

_____

_____

_____

Stop expecting others to do better when you are not willing to do better. As a leader, you cannot expect others to do better when you yourself are not better. Better begins with us. Better is contagious—when leaders build a culture for growth and demand better with their actions, the employees will follow.

Better Demands Better

When we start doing better, we can demand better. The expectation of better begins when we, ourselves, are doing better. Be very careful of people in your organization who get upset when better is demanded. You need people around you who can see better and accept the demand for better; they will add value to your organization. As a pastor, business owner, and author, I've experienced this firsthand. When better is demanded, some will quit, complain, murmur, and say you are asking for too much.

(Revelation) *Some will never put in the effort needed until it's a project of their own or they feel like they belong.*

(Matthew 25:18) *But the man who had received one bag went off, dug a hole in the ground and hid his master's money.*

Be careful of the people in your organization who only want to do better when they have a title or when there are other people around. They cannot be trusted with more because they have not taken full responsibility for the little they have been given. If we practice mediocrity in the little, we will definitely deliver mediocrity in the abundant. Once we understand that the demand for better leads to elevation and increase, maybe we will have more of a desire for better.

(Luke 16:10) *"Whoever can be trusted with very little can also be trusted with much, and whoever is dishonest with very little will also be with much."*

Better Values Better

We should not be in the same place year after year. Some have said the same thing year after year and have nothing to show for it. Perhaps they don't value what they have and choose not to improve themselves, which in the long run will leave them outdated. When we value something, we will do anything and everything to keep it. I've been married to my wife, Alisia Chery, for thirteen years and counting.

We have been through a lot as a couple; however, the one reason we are still standing is because we understand the value of our relationship-not only to ourselves, but to God, our children, and our community. I believe we will do everything and anything for the relationship to continue.

(Luke 6:31) *Do to others as you would have them do to you.*

Placing a value on better allows us to continue to grow in spite of difficult circumstances or hardships. The value we place on getting better in our relationships, organizations, workplace, and so on is vital to our longevity.

(Revelation) *There cannot be a price to what we value.*

Reflection (In your own words)

_____

_____

_____

_____

_____

Better Requires More Work

Some don't want better because better requires more work. I have started to see why some don't want better: better requires more of them: more time, sacrifice, training, and preparation.

(Luke 12:48) *But the one who does not know and does things deserving punishment will be beaten with a few blows. From everyone who has been giving much, much will be demanded; and from the one who has been entrusted with much, much more will be asked.*

Before I became a business owner, I wanted better for myself and my family. I realized if I wanted better—better pay, time with my family, and a better environment to work in—I would need to make a sacrifice and work more for a season, so I could be in a position to start my own business. Being an entrepreneur had me working more hours than I did as a nine to five employee. Being a business owner requires more out of you; however, you cannot put a price on being your own boss and doing something you really love. To be in the place I am today as my own boss, I sacrificed a lot, but it was worth it. Hard work does pay off if you stick with it.

Are you willing to put in the work for better?

If I want to be healthier, I have to put in the work to be healthy. The foods I eat have to change. My workout regimen has to change because I want to see better results. We can believe in better all we want, but if we don't accompany what we believe with work, we are insane.

(James 2:20) *You foolish person, do you want evidence that faith without deeds is useless?*

(Revelation) *Laziness is for the old you. You are better now.*

Reflection (In your own words)

_____

_____

_____

_____

_____

_____

_____

Better Requires Discipline

Webster's Dictionary defines discipline as "control gained by enforcing obedience or order." "Training that corrects, molds, or perfects the mental faculties or moral character." "To train or develop by instruction and exercise, especially in self-control."

(Revelation) *Without discipline, you are bound to go in circles.*

Reflection (In your own words)

_____

_____

_____

_____

_____

_____

(Hebrews 12:11) *No discipline seems pleasant at the time, but painful. Later on, however, it produces a harvest of righteousness and peace for those who have been trained by it.*

If we want to be better, we have to demonstrate self-control. The ability to discipline our minds, actions, and emotions is crucial in pursuing better. A synonym for the word discipline is "correct." It can be challenging to correct behaviors we have practiced for many years. Many of these behaviors come from past experiences we encountered along the way, and to be asked to correct them or have some type of discipline over them can be arduous. However, we must be willing to make the necessary adjustments. As difficult as it may seem, it's to better ourselves and others around us. When we plan for better, in whatever area it may be, we have to be disciplined enough to go through each season in order to see results.

(Proverbs 25:28) *Like a city whose walls are broken through is a person who lacks self-control.*

Another word for discipline is consistency. Can we stay consistent long enough to see a change?

(Revelation) *Consistency removes luck from the equation.*

Reflection *(In your own words)*

_____

_____

_____

_____

_____

Many depend on luck on a rainy day; others depend on being consistent with what they have set out to do or become. To be better in anything in life, you must have some type of consistency. I played college and some professional basketball. From the day I began my athletic journey in middle school and all the way through college, I remained consistent in the way I shot free throws. The days I decided to change my routine were the days I missed shots miserably.

(Revelation) *Consistency can be seen and measured.*

Reflection *(In your own words)*

_____

_____

_____

_____

Consistency can go a long way. Being consistent will definitely benefit us in one way or another. However, it benefits more when others can see the work being put in day in and day out. If we are doing what we are supposed to be doing, others will notice it and acknowledge it.

Also, if we are not doing what we are supposed to do, others will notice it and acknowledge it.

(Revelation) *Don't portray yourself to be something that you are not or are not ready to take responsibility for.*

Reflection *(In your own words)*

_____

_____

_____

_____

_____

_____

Another word for discipline is order. It's very difficult to better ourselves without having order. Better requires order. If you want better, you can't do whatever you want, whenever you want to. There must be a plan, a time, a place, and discipline. Order keeps us in line with what we say we are going to do. Order keeps us focused on the task at hand. An organization without order is dead. I have worked in different arenas in my life and one thing I've noticed is that there's always a time to clock in, a time to eat lunch, and a time to clock out. Can you imagine if that task was left to the employees? We would have chaos in the workplace and the work would never get done. We need order and discipline on our journey to better.

(1 Corinthians 14:40) *But everything should be done in decency and in order.*

Better Attracts Better

Every organization is striving to put their best foot forward because they are aware that their best attracts others. As a pastor, I cannot allow the mean person who doesn't smile to serve as an usher at the door to greet people. That's not our best. Even with a spirit-filled church, people will not have a desire to come knowing a mean person is at the door. We wouldn't even get them inside the building because I don't have my best at the door.

In today's world where everything is on social media, a church's praise and worship team has to look a certain way. The wardrobe matters, the stage presence matters, the sound matters, and the message matters.

(Revelation) *Better is just more attractive.*

Reflection (In your own words)

_____

_____

_____

_____

_____

_____

If the restaurant is clean and has great customer service, people will come. If the salesman at the local dealership is friendly and gives a great deal, people will come. People are looking for the best. And as a leader, you must strive to put your best in place to have a better outcome.

When you are better, you attract better—better people, better jobs. People want to talk to you; people want to get to know you just because you are better. It's no coincidence that companies and organizations are looking for the best to represent their brands. They know that they will get a return on their investments.

(Revelation) *People will not invest in mediocrity.*

Reflection *(In your own words)*

_____

_____

_____

_____

_____

(2 Timothy 2:15) *Do your best to present yourself to God as one approved, a worker who does not need to be ashamed and who correctly handles the word of truth.*

There are some companies that will not do business with you unless you are an approved vendor. They know that if you went through the process of getting approved, number one, your work can be trusted and, number two, your work can be measured. The school board will not do business with an unapproved vendor. Are you approved for better?

There's a Cost to Better

People spend thousands of dollars to get better. This includes training costs, hotels, and mastermind classes among others. Basketball superstar, LeBron James, spends $1,500,000 dollars a year on his body to stay in shape and play at the highest level. Better costs! If we are not willing to spend to get better, then we don't truly want to see better. If a person is offering a course, he or she had to attend school and spend long hours preparing to add value to the product they're presenting. Why would they turn around and give it to you for free?

(Revelation) *The cost for "better" is priceless.*

Reflection *(In your own words)*

_____

_____

_____

_____

_____

We spend so much money on things that add no value to us. I believe the time has come to begin to shift our minds toward better. The more we invest in ourselves and in our teams, the more fruits we will see. The expectation of better without investment is insanity.

My wife and I recently purchased a home in a nice neighborhood. The community is nice and for the most part the people who live there are nice. However, when we purchased the home, it was outdated and needed an upgrade. We decided to remodel the house from the ground up: New kitchen, bathroom, flooring, roof, etc. Because of these improvements, the value of our home has jumped tremendously and the housing market has been really helpful. We expect more for the house because of the investment we made in it. There is an old saying: "You get what you pay for."

If you are willing to invest in yourself, you'll see a difference. The places where you prioritize your investment are the places you will see a return.

Better Requires Listening

It is very difficult to lead thinking you know it all. In the journey to better, we have to be honest with ourselves because there are areas in our lives we need to improve. Listening plays a big part in getting better. When you have the attitude of a know-it-all, it's very hard to receive new information. It's also very difficult for anyone to pour into you because they can see that you are not receptive to new knowledge.

(Revelation) *We cannot lead thinking we know it all.*

Reflection *(In your own words)*

_____

_____

_____

_____

_____

_____

(Proverbs 28:26) *Those who trust in themselves are fools, but those who walk in wisdom are kept safe.*

If we are truly going after better, being humble plays a major part in growing. A humble person can receive information without being offended. How can we do better if we are not willing to listen? Any area in our lives where we assume we know it all will never grow to its full potential, because there's always room for growth.

(Revelation) *Reading and listening are essential to a better you.*

Reflection *(In your own words)*

_____

_____

_____

_____

_____

_____

A person who's always reading and searching for knowledge will always be ahead of others. Once we have decided to stop learning, we become obsolete. A company or a person who's outdated will be replaced. In order to stay current, we have to continue to reinvent ourselves to be better.

(Hosea 4:6) *My people are destroyed from lack of knowledge.*

(Revelation) *Better requires study.*

Reflection *(In your own words)*

_____

_____

_____

_____

_____

The time has come for us to position ourselves for better. This requires us to be humble in order to receive information that will elevate the individual and the organization. The people who are not willing to do better will drag the team down. It is vital that your organization grows in every department. You don't want one particular department to be growing and the others to lack.

I've sat in meetings where employees are on their phones playing games while training is taking place. How can this be? Are they really trying to get better? Or do they believe they know the information already? As leaders, we have to create an environment where trainings are relevant and the employees are engaged to become better.

Environment Matters

Not every environment is conducive for learning. Some environments are toxic, difficult to work in, and make it difficult to work with others. Not every environment will result in growth. As leaders, we have to be very careful of the environment we create for others and the environment we allow to flow in the organization. Sometimes, changing the environment or a position can have a direct impact on the growth of the organization. There are always one or two people in the workplace who make it challenging for everyone else to work with them.

(Revelation) *It takes longer for an apple to spoil by itself.*

Reflection (In your own words)

_____

_____

_____

_____

_____

_____

(Proverbs 13:20) *Walk in the wise and become wise; associate with fools and get in trouble.*

When planting a tree, you have to consider the tree and the environment you're placing the tree in. My wife loves to destroy our backyard with gardening ideas. (Just kidding!) She has these great ideas about turning our backyard into a garden with different kinds of fruits and vegetables. I, on the other hand, have a different idea of what kind of fruits I want to grow. What I've learned from her is that some fruits will not grow properly if they are in the wrong environment. Certain plants only need a few hours of sun to grow. Some need more water and more shade. When you do your research before planting, it will save you a lot of money and headache.

The same goes for us; we need the right environment to reach our highest potential. Are you in the right environment?

(Revelation) *Creating a culture for better will birth an environment for growth.*

Reflection (In your own words)

_____

_____

_____

_____

_____

_____

Better Requires Accountability

When a leader is not better, the whole team will suffer. To be better is to acknowledge areas where we are weak and place the right leaders in these areas for the betterment of the organization. Do you know what you do well? Knowing who we are and what we do best will allow us to do better with our strengths, and also give us a benchmark of where we need to improve.

(Revelation) *Stop portraying yourself as being something that you are not. Stop portraying yourself as an expert in a field when you're not.*

Reflection *(In your own words)*

_____

_____

_____

_____

_____

_____

If you don't know it, just say you don't know it. It's better to admit we don't know something than to claim we do and it turns out to be a lie. Most positions are given based on what we know, not what we think we know.

Stanley Johnson was drafted eighth overall by the Detroit Pistons in the 2015 NBA draft. He played for several teams during his four years in the NBA. During the 2019-2020 season, he was on the verge of not making an NBA roster. The scouting report on him was that he did not know who he was and wanted to play a position he was not great at. During that season, he found himself out of the league and looking for a job. The Los Angeles Lakers were looking for a great on-ball defender and Stanley Johnson's name came up. He was given a ten-day contract to prove he could play to his strength, which was defense.

Stanley took the opportunity to prove to the whole team that he could focus on his strength and make himself and the team better. Eventually, Stanley signed a two-year contract with the team because he played his position—the position that was right for him. Stanley had to make a tough decision and he was rewarded for making the right choice.

When we are better, everything and everyone around us is better. We have to begin to see doing better as a benefit not only to the individual, but also to the organization. One of the best things to do on the journey to better is to do a self-evaluation to determine where we are and what we need to do to get to where we need to be.

(Revelation) *Better requires action.*

Reflection *(In your own words)*

_____

_____

_____

_____

_____

_____

As we conclude season one, I hope and pray that you were able to receive these life-changing nuggets that will create change in your life and in your organization. Remember, there are seasons in life, and the worst thing you can do is to compare your season of growth to someone else's. Your growth may look different. Stay focused on your own journey and be consistent. Your season is right around the corner. Do you see it?

(Galatians 6:9) *Let us not become weary in doing good, for at the proper time we will reap a harvest if we do not give up.*

DISCUSSION

How can a person do better in areas they know they need to do better in?

_____

_____

_____

_____

_____

_____

What area in your life do you know you need to do better in?

_____

_____

_____

_____

_____

_____

What does "better" look like to you?

_____

_____

_____

_____

_____

_____

What are the benefits of bettering yourself?

_____

_____

_____

What are the causes and effects of not getting better?

Whose responsibility is it to do better?

Whose responsibility is it to get the information to do better?

Which individual(s) in your life can help you do better?

_____

_____

_____

_____

_____

_____

Are you confident that once you know better you'll do better? How?

_____

_____

_____

_____

_____

_____

_____

What training have you taken or currently are taking to better yourself or your organization?

_____

_____

_____

_____

_____

_____

_____

After reading this chapter, what have you learned?

_____

_____

_____

_____

Define growth:

Define improvement:

Define attraction:

Define exceed:

Define finish:

Define test:

Define forward:

Define elevate:

_____

_____

_____

_____

_____

_____

Define journey:

_____

_____

_____

_____

_____

_____

Define discipline:

_____

_____

_____

_____

_____

_____

Define accountability:

_____

_____

_____

_____

_____

SEASON 2

MATURITY MATTERS

The quicker we mature, the quicker we can achieve our goals. As we enter season two on our journey to better, I want us to focus on the word **maturity**.

Webster's Dictionary defines maturity as "the quality or state of being mature, full development."

(Revelation) *Maturity helps us to keep what we have gained. When we are mature, better becomes easier to pursue and maintain.*

Reflection (In your own words)

_____

_____

_____

_____

_____

_____

For many of us, the journey to better may not feel good at the moment, but it must be done. We cannot stay the same and expect better. Growing is a lifestyle that is continual. And the more we grow, the better we become. Have you ever walked into your office and said to yourself, "I have to do better?" I do it all the time because I am my biggest critic.

(Revelation) *Some will never grow because they are not rooted long enough.*

Reflection *(In your own words)*

_____

_____

_____

_____

_____

_____

Some will never grow because they are not rooted long enough. Every little thing that happens in their lives, they uproot themselves because they don't like how it feels or they don't see enough progress. How can we grow in anything in life if every time someone says something we don't like, we get up and leave? Better requires maturity. We have to stay long enough to see real growth. The reason you are there in the first place is because you believe you can grow there, so don't allow anyone to cause you to miss your season of growth because of immaturity.

(Revelation) *Don't go where you are tolerated, go where you are appreciated. Where you are appreciated, you will be challenged; being challenged will cause growth.*

Reflection *(In your own words)*

_____

_____

_____

_____

Maturity allows us to pursue what is needed for growth. If we don't pursue growth, we will not be able to sustain the longevity of anything. We don't simply pursue better just for a position or a title, we seek after better because we know in the long run, better will allow us to walk in doors that mediocrity has kept us from for too long.

(Revelation) *When we are better, we reduce the chance of mediocrity.*

Reflection *(In your own words)*

_____

_____

_____

_____

_____

As a father, husband, pastor, and business owner, I don't have a lot of room to not get it right. I know I am not perfect and I am not trying to be; however, when my wife and children are depending on me to be better, mediocrity is not an option. Even when I don't want to do the right thing, I have to be mature enough to understand that my decisions have a direct impact on not just me, but my entire family.

(Revelation) *Immaturity requires supervision.*

Reflection *(In your own words)*

_____

_____

_____

_____

_____

One of the reasons I watch my children as they cross streets is because they are not mature enough to do it by themselves. In the same way, in every organization, a position is given based on who can manage their job with little to no supervision.

Are you mature enough to handle what comes with the position? To do better, we have to be willing to deal with obstacles as they come. Maturity allows us to handle the pressure of life and to be able to make life-changing decisions without compromising our integrity and the well-being of our family and organization.

(Revelation) *How we deal with obstacles will determine how quickly we get to being better.*

Reflection *(In your own words)*

_____

_____

_____

_____

_____

_____

The purpose for better is for increase, growth, and forward movement. When we are growing spiritually, it's easier for other areas in our lives to grow as well. There's a time for milk and there's a time for meat. It would look silly if a grown person was still drinking from a baby's bottle. Imagine going to a restaurant for dinner and they serve you the food in an infant's bottle.

(Revelation) *Immaturity can easily be detected.*

Reflection *(In your own words)*

_____
_____
_____
_____
_____
_____

(Isaiah 28:9-10) *"Whom shall he teach knowledge? And whom shall he make to understand doctrine? Them that are weaned from milk, and drawn from the breast. For the precept must upon precept, precept upon precept; line upon line, line upon line; here a little, and there a little:"*

(1 Corinthians 13:11) *"When I was a child, I thought like a child, I reasoned like a child. When I become a man, I put the ways of childhood behind me."*

Stop asking for milk; the time for milk is over. We have to grow and mature in order to experience better. Many of us don't see growth because we are still dealing with immaturity in certain areas in our lives. I am looking for the new in you. In order to get rid of the old in you, it's going to require more work, more dedication, and more maturity.

(Revelation) *Growth can be measured.*

Reflection *(In your own words)*

_____
_____
_____
_____

Doing the same thing year after year and expecting a different outcome is insanity. To do better is to reevaluate one's self and put a plan in place to get better. It's very difficult to see change if we don't put in the work for change.

(Revelation) *Stop looking for a raise or promotion, when we still need to be better and add value to ourselves.*

Reflection *(In your own words)*

_____

_____

_____

_____

_____

_____

Spiritual Maturity

How can we call ourselves mature Christians when we are so easily offended and distracted? A seasoned believer should have developed self-control over time. When a person is mature, he or she understands that the enemy is looking for an entry point to cause them to retreat and give up on purpose. We need to do better on how we react when we are wronged.

(Revelation) *Offense is an opportunity to grow.*

Reflection *(In your own words)*

_____

_____

_____

_____

_____

_____

(Proverbs 19:11) *A person's wisdom yields patience; it is to one's glory to overlook an offense.*

As Christians, we should deal with offense differently. We should be more forgiving, more lenient, more compassionate, and more restorative. We are too cutthroat when we are offended. We act worse than unsaved people. For example, when some are offended, their behaviors change, the way they talk changes. They begin to curse, scream, and yell at others. We have to be better. We are an example to the world and we can do better.

I've been in church all my life and if I began to tell you the stories of so-called mature Christians acting out of character, you would not believe me. People get offended for the smallest things- from their birthdays not being acknowledged, to clothing, song selections, and so on. We have to be better.

(Revelation) *Complaining is not better.*

Reflection *(In your own words)*

_____

_____

_____

_____

We Need to do Better With Forgiveness

Forgiveness is part of growth. When we learn how to forgive, we can grow spiritually in every area. A person who doesn't forgive will be bitter, hurt, mean, offended, nasty, unwilling, and, most of all, prideful. It is very difficult for this person to be better.

(Ephesians 4:32) *Be kind and compassionate to one another, forgiving each other, just as in Christ God forgave you.*

(Revelation) *Forgiveness is for you.*

Reflection (In your own words)

_____

_____

_____

_____

_____

_____

Having to work in an environment where leaders dislike each other can be very toxic and detrimental to the organization. As Christians, we have an obligation to forgive our brothers and sisters when they have wronged us.

(Revelation) *Forgiveness gives access to be forgiven.*

We need to do better with how we communicate with one another

As leaders, we have to learn how to speak with one another. We speak to people at work better than we converse with people at church. If we don't know how to communicate with each other, how then, can we do better or grow? In everything, communication plays a big role in the success of the organization. If we want to grow, we have to learn how to communicate effectively and with respect.

(Revelation) *The way you deliver your words matters.*

There are two types of communication: verbal and non-verbal. Verbal communication is what comes out of our mouths. How we articulate what we feel and how we give information. In order for the receiver to receive or accept what is being said, the delivery and tone matter.

(Amos 3:3) *Do two walk together unless they have agreed to do so?*

(Revelation) *You cannot speak to people in any type of way and expect them to receive what is being said.*

Reflection *(In your own words)*

_____

_____

_____

_____

_____

_____

Non-verbal communication is done through body language and eye contact. Some would say, "I did not say anything." What they fail to realize is their body language said it all. Their eye contact displayed openly what was in their heart. There is an adage that says, "If looks could kill." As leaders, don't kill anyone with the way you look at them.

I had to learn not to carry my emotions on my face. If I was upset or mad at something, onlookers would clearly see it on my face or in my body language. Maturity allows you to observe the situation and deal with it at the proper time.

(Revelation) *Not every situation needs to be discussed publicly or openly.*

Reflection *(In your own words)*

_____

_____

_____

_____

_____

_____

In my experience as a leader, non-verbal communication can cause more harm than actually saying what you feel.

(Matthew 15:18) *But the things that come out of a person's mouth come from the heart, and these defile them.*

(Revelation) *Be careful of people demanding better from you, but when better is demanded from them, it's a problem.*

Reflection (In your own words)

_____

_____

_____

_____

_____

_____

We Need to do Better on How We Take Constructive Criticism
Constructive criticism, if given in the right way and context, can be beneficial to the listener. Honest criticism is not an attack.

(Revelation) *Better requires criticism.*

Reflection (In your own words)

_____

_____

_____

_____

_____

_____

My wife tells me all the time to check my grammar. I could have easily gotten offended by her words. Instead, I received the criticism because I know she's trying to make me better. In addition to wanting me to look better, she also looks better because we are one.

(Revelation) *Be careful of people demanding better but not willing to give better.*

Reflection *(In your own words)*

_____

_____

_____

_____

_____

_____

When you become part of an organization, everything you do is a reflection of the organization. So, when corrections are made, it is for the growth of the entity. Let us do better on how we receive criticism because even though it may feel like an attack, if it's done with sincerity and honesty, it should be received as an opportunity to grow.

However, some corrections or criticism may seem harsh because the expectation has not been met after several attempts.

(Revelation) *One of the hardest things for a teacher or a leader to do is to repeat themselves over and over again for the same thing.*

Reflection *(In your own words)*

_____
_____
_____
_____
_____
_____

(Hebrews 6:1) *Therefore let us move beyond the elementary teachings about Christ and be taken forward to maturity, not laying again the foundation of repentance from acts that lead to death, and of faith in God.*

(Revelation) *It's very difficult to accept criticism from a person who's mediocre.*

Reflection *(In your own words)*

_____
_____
_____
_____
_____
_____

In this season, we talked about growing spiritually in every area of our lives. I believe if we are growing and doing better in our spiritual walk, then the other areas will follow. Another way to grow spiritually is to grow in the word of God. Without the word of God, it will be difficult to grow. We have to read and apply it daily. Meditate on the Scriptures day and night in order for the word to penetrate our minds and hearts.

(Matthew 4:4) *But He answered, 'It is written, "Man shall not live by bread alone, but by every word that comes from the mouth of God."'*

Some Key Elements to Consider in Growing Spiritually and to do Better.

Humility and gratitude.

Read the Bible daily. Matthew 4:4; Timothy 3:16

Prayer and worship.

Spend time with people who want to grow.

Serve and give.

Repentance.

Forgiveness.

Participate in church community and activities.

DISCUSSION

How do we do better in areas of our lives we know need improvement, but can't seem to get better?

_____

_____

_____

_____

_____

_____

How well do you communicate with others?

_____

_____

_____

_____

Do you struggle with forgiveness?

How well do you handle constructive criticism?

What plans or strategies do you have in place for a better you?

If you can envision yourself doing better in your life, what would it look like?

How do you add value to your organization or workplace?

Are you mature enough to handle the responsibilities that are required for better?

What do you believe God is calling you to do?

Are you afraid? If so, why?

After reading this chapter, what have you learned?

Define dishonest:

Define advancement:

Define beyond:

_____

_____
_____
_____
_____
_____

Define excellence:

_____
_____
_____
_____
_____
_____

Define transcend:

_____
_____
_____
_____
_____
_____

Define skillful:

_____
_____
_____
_____
_____

Define competent:

_____

_____

_____

_____

_____

_____

_____

_____

Define mediocrity:

_____

_____

_____

_____

_____

_____

_____

_____

Define professional:

_____

_____

_____

_____

_____

_____

_____

_____

Define proficient:

_____

_____

_____

_____

_____

_____

_____

_____

_____

_____

_____

_____

Define accountability:

_____

_____

_____

_____

_____

_____

_____

_____

_____

_____

_____

_____

_____

SEASON 3

DO BETTER STARTS NOW.

(Ecclesiastes 11:4-6) *"Whoever watches the wind will not plant; whoever looks at the clouds will not reap. As you do not know the path of the wind, or how the body is formed in a mother's womb, so you cannot understand the work of God, the Maker of all things. Sow your seed in the morning, and in the evening let your hands not be idle, for you do not know which will succeed, whether this or that, or whether both will do equally well."*

(Revelation) *The longer it takes for us to get better, the longer it will take to be better.*

Reflection *(In your own words)*

_____

_____

_____

_____

_____

_____

How much longer are you going to say "I don't know?" When are you going to decide to be better? Whatever you want to do or be better at, you must take the time to invest in it now to see and experience better. Whether it's in friendships, relationships, buying a house, getting a diploma, or getting healthier—do better right now!

(Revelation) *The time for better is now, not tomorrow. Tomorrow is not promised.*

Reflection *(In your own words)*

_____

_____

_____

_____

_____

_____

(Ephesians 5:15-17) *"Be very careful, then, how you live—not as unwise but as wise, making the most of every opportunity, because the days are evil. Therefore, do not be foolish, but understand what the Lord's will is."*

Stop watching the wind. Whatever God has asked you to do, do it now! Don't say you have time. There's a time for everything. There is a time to activate what's for you, there's also a season for you and what you have been called to do.

(Ecclesiastes 9:10) *"Whatever your hand finds to do, do it with all you might, for in the realm of the dead, where you are going, there is neither working nor planning nor knowledge nor wisdom."*

Don't sit and say, "Whatever is for me is for me," like what is for you will wait on you. We have to take advantage of the time we currently have. If you are still breathing, you have something to do.

(Revelation) *Time is not waiting on anyone.*

Reflection *(In your own words)*

_____

_____

_____

_____

_____

_____

Don't get caught up looking at the clouds. If you have an opportunity to plan today, don't wait for tomorrow—plan now, and do now.

(Revelation) *When we plant now, we give tomorrow's rain a chance to water today's labor.*

Reflection *(In your own words)*

_____

_____

_____

_____

_____

_____

Some would say, "Let me wait for the right time"—but the right time is now. Whatever issues you are dealing with, whether in marriage, finance, business, or health, deal with it now!

(Revelation) *If you have been given the opportunity to choose better, choose it now. Some people around the world don't have that choice.*

_____

_____

_____

_____

_____

_____

(John 9:4-5) *"As long as it is day, we must do the works of Him who sent me. Night is coming, when no one can work. While I am in the world, I am the light of the world."*

What are you waiting for? The right time? The right feelings? The right person to validate you? Stop waiting for people to tell you something that God has already told you.

What is God asking you to do? If God put it in your heart, He will provide for you. It is our responsibility to develop and grow the gifts that were given to us. God is counting on us to develop and do what He has given us to do. I want you to think about the following: what God is asking us to do is not just for us but for everyone connected to us. God has given us the opportunity to bless everyone we come in contact with. However, we cannot be a blessing to others if we are not better.

How do we do better in areas of our lives where we know we need to do better, but can't seem to do so?

Better is determination on purpose.
Better is following instruction.
Better is refocusing your focus.
Better is you.

Better is consistency.

Better is not a title.

Better is the desire from within to be better.

Better is pushing through the obstacles.

Better is not accepting mediocrity.

Better is a lifestyle.

Even when we want to do better and have a desire to do so, something or someone is always fighting us in our journey.

(Galatians 5:17) *For the flesh desires what is contrary to the Spirit, and the Spirit what is contrary to the flesh. They are in conflict with each other, so that you are not to do whatever you want.*

(Revelation) *It's not just our flesh we have to worry about.*

Reflection (In your own words)

_____

_____

_____

_____

DISCUSSION

How much money do you spend yearly to better yourself and/or your team?

_____

_____

_____

_____

What sacrifices have you made in the past or are willing to make now to do better?

_____
_____
_____
_____
_____
_____
_____
_____

Are you a procrastinator?

_____
_____
_____
_____
_____
_____
_____
_____

Are you willing to invest in yourself for a better you?

_____
_____
_____
_____
_____
_____
_____
_____

How many books do you read yearly? List the recent titles.

_____
_____
_____
_____
_____
_____

Who do you listen to daily?

_____
_____
_____
_____
_____
_____

Are you a great listener? Explain

_____
_____
_____
_____
_____
_____

Are you a great note taker? Explain

_____
_____
_____
_____

After a meeting, do you return to your notes? Explain why or why not

_____

_____

_____

_____

_____

After reading this chapter, what have you learned?

_____

_____

_____

_____

_____

Define responsibility:

_____

_____

_____

_____

_____

Define pursue:

_____

_____

_____

_____

Define dedication:

_____
_____
_____
_____
_____
_____

Define sacrifice:

_____
_____
_____
_____
_____
_____

Define time:

_____
_____
_____
_____
_____
_____

Define consistency:

_____
_____
_____
_____
_____

Define procrastination:

_____

_____

_____

_____

_____

_____

_____

_____

_____

_____

_____

_____

Define priorities:

_____

_____

_____

_____

_____

_____

_____

_____

_____

_____

_____

_____

Define dedication:

_____
_____
_____
_____
_____
_____
_____
_____
_____
_____
_____
_____
_____

Define devoted:

_____
_____
_____
_____
_____
_____
_____
_____
_____
_____
_____
_____
_____

SEASON 4

YOUR ENVIRONMENT MATTERS

In the process of getting better, your environment matters. The people you have around you have as much to do with your success and your destruction as you do.

(1 Corinthians 15:33) *Do not be deceived: Bad company corrupts good character.*

(Revelation) *If you are smarter than all your friends, you don't really have friends, you have enablers.*

Reflection *(In your own words)*

_____

_____

_____

_____

_____

_____

We have to be very careful of the company we keep. There are friends that will allow you to do whatever you want to do. This is very dangerous because doing whatever you want to do doesn't get you to do better. This actually leads you to stay stagnant year after year.

(Revelation) *Mediocrity is contagious.*

Reflection (In your own words)

_____

_____

_____

_____

_____

_____

It's extremely difficult to excel when everyone around you wants to be average. We need people in our lives who are not afraid to inform us about areas we need to improve in.

When we have people in our lives who will challenge us, growing and doing better will be inevitable. When I was in college, I had two special friends, Marvin and Sherard, who kept me on my feet and would do anything for me as I would for them.

I remember one incident where they challenged me to finish college. You see, they graduated college before me and they were adamant about me finishing as well. I wanted to go play basketball professionally; however, I only had a few credits left to graduate. I remember one evening I was hanging out with them and, out of the blue, they stood up and told me to my face that I had to finish school if I wanted to continue to hang out with them. They gave an ultimatum! I knew they meant it from a place of love. I knew what they were saying would make me better and I took it upon myself to finish school.

I thank them every time I see them. They are the kind of friends I needed and still need today. The same way they are bold about telling me to get better, I am bold about telling them to get better. If we are going to be around each other, we need each other to be the best we can be. That's the kind of environment and friendship we need to grow.

Ask yourself, what kind of friends do you have?

(Revelation) *Only iron can sharpen iron.*

Reflection *(In your own words)*

_____

_____

_____

_____

_____

_____

A well-sharpened knife is able to do what it was designed to do. When a knife is dull, it becomes hard to use and makes you do more work. In the same way, we need people around us who are going to sharpen us to be better. This way, we can be the best we can be and function properly.

My friend, Perry Tima, came to our church and said something that was profound. He said, **"Wood doesn't sharpen iron."** What he was trying to say was that you cannot use wood to sharpen iron—wood is not meant to do that. The wood's function is to hold the grip of the knife, not to sharpen it. When wood remains in contact with iron for a long time, it creates rust around the iron. Ask yourself, "How many of your friends are iron and how many are wood?"

(Revelation) *Some of us are rusty because of what's around us or holding us together.*

Reflection *(In your own words)*

_____

_____

_____

_____

Most people reject anyone who attempts to challenge them to do better. I don't know about you; but I want people around me who will challenge me to do better and be better. Better requires us to cut off who and what is not good in our lives in order to grow.

(John 15:2) *He cuts off every branch in me that bears no fruits, while every branch that does not bear fruit, he prunes so that it will be even more fruitful.*

Be careful of the friends or people who are placed in our lives strategically to keep us comfortable with being mediocre.

(Revelation) *Better begins in the mind.*

Reflection *(In your own words)*

In one of my favorite movies, *Coming to America*, the character played by Eddie Murphy was getting married to a woman he'd never met. In Zamunda, it is tradition for the parents of the grooms to select their brides for them. The woman who was selected for Eddie Murphy (the prince) was very beautiful and trained since birth on how to be a queen. When Eddie Murphy met her, he was excited and wanted to speak with her just before the ceremony began. During the brief conversation, he realized that she was trained to do everything he said to do and even if told her not to, she would not listen. Eddie realized that this woman would not make him better because she was trained to do whatever he said. He ended up going to America to find someone who would challenge his intellect.

Who is sharpening you? Who's challenging you? Who's your mentor? Your trainer? People who don't want better don't like people who challenge them.

Better Requires a Mentor.

Do you have a mentor? It is very important to submit ourselves to someone who can mentor us into becoming better. To do better requires constant challenges from people who have already done what we are trying to accomplish. A mentor will hold you accountable for your growth. A mentor will instruct you on what to do and how to do it. A mentor will pour wisdom into you from life lessons and experiences that you only can get from a person who has been there and done that.

A mentor will activate certain gifts in you that you never knew were there. Samuel had an Eli, Elisha had an Elijah, Moses had a Jethro, Joshua had a Moses and so on. Everyone needs a mentor. Don't allow pride to stop you from reaching out to someone you know can help you.

Don't look for a promotion if you have not been faithful in your current position.

Just because you have learned something, does not mean you are growing. Growth comes with time and experience.

How Do We Do Better?
Acknowledge that you need to do better
Self-evaluation in every area
Action
Prayer
Accountability (Mentor) friend

DISCUSSION

Is your environment conducive to helping you get better?

_____
_____
_____
_____
_____
_____

Do you have a mentor?

_____
_____
_____
_____
_____

Do the friends you have in your life push you to be better?

_____
_____
_____

_____

_____

_____

Are you willing to cut the people in your life who are dragging you down?

_____

_____

_____

_____

_____

Are you willing to make life changing decisions to better your life? Explain.

_____

_____

_____

_____

_____

List some of the things you do very well?

_____

_____

_____

_____

_____

Who or what is stopping you from getting better?

_____

How's your mental health?

What reward system do you have for yourself and your achievements?

Define educate:

Define environment:

_____
_____
_____
_____
_____
_____

Define achievement:

_____
_____
_____
_____
_____
_____

Define refine:

_____
_____
_____
_____
_____
_____

Define develop:

_____
_____
_____
_____
_____

Define revamp:

_____

_____

_____

_____

_____

_____

Define revise:

_____

_____

_____

_____

_____

_____

Define enhance:

_____

_____

_____

_____

_____

_____

Define upgrade:

_____

_____

_____

_____

Define cultivate:

Define relevant:

CONCLUSION

In this manual, we talked about four seasons to a better you. In every season, we are supposed to learn something in order to grow. And the moment we stop growing is the moment we begin to stagnate.

If we truly want to grow, move forward in our lives, and make ourselves and our organizations better, we have to accept that the responsibility is ours. It is our duty to seek the knowledge we need and to make the necessary changes, commitments, and sacrifices for better. It's not going to be easy, but nothing worth doing is.

You've got this!

Better is always only one step-one decision away.

I pray this book has helped you, inspired you, and challenged you to be better, to reach for better, and to DO BETTER.

NOTES

NOTES

NOTES

NOTES

NOTES

NOTES

NOTES

NOTES

NOTES

NOTES

NOTES

NOTES

NOTES

NOTES

NOTES

NOTES

NOTES

NOTES

NOTES